COMPUTE
a
DESIGN

DECIMALS

Patricia Wright

JACOBS PUBLISHING COMPANY, INC.
PHOENIX   ARIZONA

AUTHOR   Patricia Wright

Patricia Wright is presently teaching at Thirkill Elementary School in Soda Springs, Idaho. She formerly taught at Dixon Junior High School in Provo, Utah. She is also the author of the popular book **SEARCH n SHADE.** She has applied the "search n shade" concept to this new book **COMPUTE a DESIGN: Decimals** in order to provide a comprehensive review and practice program for students needing remediation in the fundamental operations with whole numbers.

COVER DESIGN   Robert E. Haberer

Robert E. Haberer is an art teacher at Camelback High School in Phoenix, Arizona. He was formerly the Director of Instructional Materials for the Phoenix Union High School District.

ISBN 0-918272-13-0

TABLE OF CONTENTS

1 ADDITION

Name_____

7.729	9.9	.65	6.705	8.6	7.67	9.97	5.79	7.77	9.97
9.99	6.705	9.97	5.79	7.77	9.9	5.876	6.705	7.98	8.97
7.67	6.886	7.77	7.98	.65	5.79	7.67	9.99	8.89	8.6
8.97	8.6	7.729	6.886	5.79	5.876	8.97	7.98	7.729	6.886
5.79	8.89	9.99	5.876	6.705	9.97	.65	8.89	9.99	.65
.65	5.876	.65	7.729	9.9	8.89	8.6	5.79	5.876	5.79
8.6	7.67	9.97	7.77	7.98	7.67	9.9	7.729	7.98	7.67
8.97	9.99	7.77	7.98	8.97	9.99	6.705	6.886	8.97	6.886
8.6	6.705	9.97	8.97	9.97	7.729	9.99	7.67	9.97	7.729
8.89	6.886	7.77	7.98	8.89	9.9	6.705	6.886	8.97	9.9

■
.23
+.42

◪
5.4
+3.2

◳
4.52
+3.25

◸
4.002
+2.703

◩
4.774
+2.112

■
3.44
+2.35

◹
5.24
+4.73

◺
8.14
+ .83

◸
6.34
+2.55

◿
3.524
+4.205

◿
9.6
+ .3

◺
4.26
+3.41

◩
4.47
+5.52

■
5.635
+ .241

◸
5.76
+2.22

2 ADDITION

Name_____

.17	113.1	49.629	.37	.17	128.21	111.3	.37	49.629	113.1
69.6	.85	9.43	.35	.85	9.43	.35	.85	9.43	22.2
111.3	9.43	22.2	1.4	22.2	104.4	.824	69.6	.35	113.1
1.4	.85	.37	.73	111.3	113.1	.73	111.3	.85	82.7
.17	.35	82.7	49.629	.85	9.43	.37	1.4	9.43	.37
104.4	9.43	128.21	69.6	9.43	.35	82.7	49.629	.85	.824
111.3	9.43	.824	.73	104.4	.824	.73	104.4	.35	128.21
1.4	.85	.37	.17	113.1	49.629	128.21	111.3	9.43	22.2
49.629	9.43	.35	9.43	.85	.35	9.43	.85	.35	128.21
69.6	82.7	1.4	22.2	69.6	82.7	104.4	.824	1.4	82.7

■ 8.86
+ .57

� 53.7
+15.9

◣ 62.5
+50.6

◪ 64.8
+17.9

◸ 72.9
+38.4

■ .26
+.09

◺ .6
+.8

◣ .28
+.09

◣ 55.92
+72.29

◸ .576
+.248

◣ 49.467
+   .162

◸ .7
+21.5

◪ .08
+.09

■ .58
+.27

◣ 20.7
+83.7

3 ADDITION

139.73	55.2	408	1.339	111.01	404.4	408	81.3	55.2	14.6
161.41	87.6	14.6	85.3	87.6	111.01	69.6	82.7	69.6	74.82
111.01	408	1.339	74.82	1.3	85.02	81.3	85.02	1.3	69.6
404.4	63.5	85.3	85.02	82.7	413	82.7	413	82.7	413
63.5	111.01	63.5	1.3	85.02	81.3	85.02	1.3	63.5	85.3
87.6	404.4	413	69.6	413	82.7	413	111.01	404.4	63.5
81.3	85.02	1.3	85.02	81.3	85.02	82.7	87.6	63.5	111.01
81.3	82.7	82.7	82.7	69.6	413	14.6	408	1.339	63.5
55.2	1.3	1.3	81.3	111.01	161.41	87.6	74.82	85.3	139.73
14.6	74.82	69.6	139.73	404.4	63.5	85.3	1.339	55.2	161.41

■ 54.4
+   .8

◫ 159.3
+248.7

◳ .454
+.885

◨ .62 + .68 = _____   ◪ 17.8 + 64.9 = _____

■ .9 + 13.7 = _____   ■ 65.24 + 9.58 = _____

◺ .4 + 84.9 = _____   ◪ 260.4 + 152.6 = _____

◳ 31.9 + 55.7 = _____   ◨ 61.04 + 23.98 = _____

◪ 15.9 + 53.7 = _____   ◤ 32.64 + 107.09 = _____

◪ 54.5 + 26.8 = _____   ◤ 54.63 + 106.78 = _____

4 ADDITION

Name_____

.908	.86	.49	43.74	14.05	5.122	7.34	43.34	37.83	43.74
5.122	7.34	85.22	37.83	1.033	93.99	85.22	14.05	44.103	14.55
43.74	14.55	1.033	93.99	1.66	1.033	1.66	93.99	.86	.908
37.83	43.74	14.55	.86	.49	43.34	14.55	.86	7.34	85.22
.49	5.122	7.34	44.103	14.05	85.22	.49	44.103	37.83	44.103
85.22	.908	93.99	1.033	43.34	.49	1.033	1.66	43.74	14.05
44.103	14.55	1.66	43.74	14.55	5.122	.908	93.99	5.122	.49
.86	.908	1.033	85.22	7.34	43.34	37.83	1.66	44.103	14.55
43.74	14.05	43.34	.908	.86	14.05	43.74	.908	5.122	.908
37.83	44.103	37.83	5.122	.49	44.103	14.05	.86	7.34	85.22

■ .34 +.693

◺ .09 +.4

◸ 4.5 + .622

◤ 40.94 + 3.163   ◹ 13.95 + .6   ■ 93.4 + .59   ◺ .4 +.508

◤ 84.3 + .92   ◺ .56 +.3   ◹ 1.1 +42.24   ◹ 29.6 + 8.23

◤ .2 +43.54   ◿ .6 +13.45   ■ .96 +.7   ◺ 6.6 + .74

5 ADDITION

186.95	35.1	440.61	17.59	35.1	78.14	7.365	36.96	41.06	86.95
7.365	55.12	186.95	.95	.65	55.12	43.18	1.274	186.95	61.73
36.96	.95	17.59	7.365	36.96	186.95	.95	61.73	78.14	35.1
186.95	17.59	35.1	16.37	440.61	43.18	78.14	17.59	41.06	55.12
.65	7.365	36.96	55.12	35.1	1.274	61.73	.95	.65	86.95
43.18	440.61	17.59	78.14	61.73	55.12	.65	7.365	55.12	36.96
35.1	1.274	.95	61.73	86.95	7.365	16.37	440.61	17.59	.95
440.61	61.73	78.14	186.95	17.59	35.1	36.96	.95	186.95	7.365
78.14	.95	43.18	86.95	7.365	55.12	186.95	17.59	.65	440.61
41.06	1.274	.65	36.96	41.06	36.96	.95	35.1	55.12	.95

■
$$186.5$$
$$+\quad .45$$

◨
$$86.05$$
$$+\quad .9$$

◣
$$4.26$$
$$+36.8$$

◩ .2 + .45 = _____

◲ 69.0 + 9.14 = _____

■ .05 + .9 = _____

◨ 34.9 + 2.06 = _____

◩ 34.6 + .5 = _____

■ 3.5 + 14.09 = _____

◣ .6 + .674 = _____

◪ 7.34 + .025 = _____

�￧ .2 + 42.98 = _____

◪ 436.5 + 4.11 = _____

◩ .82 + 54.3 = _____

◣ 29.6 + 32.13 = _____

Name_____

90.4	40.2	9.42	9.871	35.87	47.7	39.2	40.2	9.42	90.4
20.52	39.2	3.35	17.47	25.4	97.25	20.52	35.87	9.871	17.47
90.26	25.4	90.4	26.9	23.8	90.26	47.7	90.4	20.52	26.9
90.4	47.7	23.8	9.871	17.47	40.2	39.2	3.35	35.87	9.871
35.87	3.35	26.9	47.7	9.871	90.4	23.8	47.7	26.9	90.26
17.47	40.2	9.42	20.52	9.871	39.2	25.4	40.2	9.42	20.52
39.2	40.2	9.42	90.4	23.8	3.35	90.4	97.25	17.47	9.871
20.52	35.87	9.871	25.4	17.47	20.52	97.25	39.2	90.26	9.42
47.7	39.2	97.25	23.8	26.9	90.26	3.35	25.4	9.871	26.9
9.871	3.35	35.87	90.4	9.42	40.2	39.2	47.7	23.8	90.4

■
$$\begin{array}{r} 90 \\ +\ .4 \\ \hline \end{array}$$

◪
$$\begin{array}{r} .42 \\ +9 \\ \hline \end{array}$$

◤
$$\begin{array}{r} 47 \\ +\ .7 \\ \hline \end{array}$$

◹ 38 + 2.2 = _____   ◤ 35 + .87 = _____   ■ .2 + 39 = _____

◣ 17 + .47 = _____   ◤ 90 + .26 = _____   ◺ .35 + 3 = _____

◺ 5.25 + 92 = _____   ◤ 23 + .8 = _____   ◹ 15 + 5.52 = _____

◹ .9 + 26 = _____   ■ 9 + .871 = _____   ◤ 25 + .4 = _____

Name_____

28.814	64.55	34.15	28.814	64.55	34.15	28.814	64.55	34.15	28.814
34.15	28.814	21.27	54.39	28.814	34.15	24.94	23.42	64.55	28.814
64.55	24.94	1.52	6.34	50.7	12.63	1.52	100.13	50.7	34.15
28.814	36.43	24.94	23.42	54.55	88.88	21.27	54.39	54.55	64.55
34.15	12.63	54.39	12.63	50.7	24.94	23.42	24.94	50.7	28.814
64.55	100.13	1.52	54.55	88.88	54.55	1.52	6.34	36.43	34.15
28.814	64.55	21.27	50.7	64.55	34.15	24.94	50.7	28.814	64.55
34.15	54.55	23.42	34.15	28.814	64.55	28.814	24.94	88.88	34.15
64.55	28.814	100.13	50.7	12.63	54.39	21.27	1.52	64.55	28.814
28.814	64.55	34.15	54.55	1.52	100.13	36.43	34.15	28.814	64.55

■
$$\begin{array}{r} 5.01 \\ .2 \\ 23.6 \\ + \quad .004 \\ \hline \end{array}$$

◪
$$\begin{array}{r} 17.47 \\ 24.9 \\ .02 \\ +12 \\ \hline \end{array}$$

◪
$$\begin{array}{r} 3.05 \\ .07 \\ 3.2 \\ + \quad .02 \\ \hline \end{array}$$

◸
$$\begin{array}{r} .17 \\ 1.7 \\ 17 \\ + \ 2.4 \\ \hline \end{array}$$

◸
$$\begin{array}{r} 80 \\ .08 \\ .8 \\ + \ 8 \\ \hline \end{array}$$

■
$$\begin{array}{r} 42.5 \\ .03 \\ +22.02 \\ \hline \end{array}$$

◪
$$\begin{array}{r} .9 \\ 26 \\ 23 \\ + \quad .8 \\ \hline \end{array}$$

◪ $47 + .35 + 2.2 + 5 =$ _____

◪ $3.6 + .03 + 92 + 4.5 =$ _____

◹ $.42 + 11 + 1.21 =$ _____

◹ $.06 + .56 + .6 + .3 =$ _____

◹ $5.52 + 7.5 + .92 + 11 =$ _____

◸ $32 + .03 + .2 + 4.2 =$ _____

■ $13 + .09 + 21.02 + .04 =$ _____

◪ $15 + 5.52 + 2.2 + .7 =$ _____

7.151	8.42	23.63	16.66	89.42	21.32	17.42	7.78	99.23	85.09
8.42	17.42	18.34	3.30	99.23	7.151	1.027	18.34	16.66	16.66
85.09	21.32	89.42	21.32	1.027	1.7	21.32	89.42	21.32	17.42
3.30	99.23	18.34	89.42	85.09	8.42	21.32	18.34	8.42	27.43
18.34	23.63	7.78	3.30	1.027	1.7	27.43	1.7	1.027	21.32
89.42	17.42	85.09	17.42	99.23	7.151	16.66	7.151	85.09	89.42
8.42	1.027	89.42	18.34	7.78	3.30	18.34	21.32	23.63	99.23
27.43	21.32	18.34	21.32	16.66	8.42	89.42	21.32	89.42	1.7
3.30	1.7	89.42	7.151	7.78	23.63	16.66	18.34	1.027	7.78
1.7	23.63	17.42	1.027	21.32	89.42	3.30	85.09	27.43	7.78

$$\begin{array}{r} 66.02 \\ +23.4 \\ \hline \end{array}$$

$$\begin{array}{r} 82 \\ +\ 3.09 \\ \hline \end{array}$$

$$\begin{array}{r} 1.6 \\ +22.03 \\ \hline \end{array}$$

$$\begin{array}{r} 6.301 \\ +\ .85 \\ \hline \end{array}$$

$$\begin{array}{r} 18.42 \\ +\ 9.01 \\ \hline \end{array}$$

$$\begin{array}{r} 19.3 \\ +\ 2.02 \\ \hline \end{array}$$

$$\begin{array}{r} 96.83 \\ +\ 2.4 \\ \hline \end{array}$$

.06 + 3.24 = _____

.8 + .9 = _____

6.92 + .06 + .8 = _____

17 + .42 = _____

.39 + 8.03 = _____

.645 + .382 = _____

8.6 + .06 + 8 = _____

6.04 + 12.3 = _____

9 SUBTRACTION

.5	.513	.42	.4	.62	.07	.24	.4	.62	.5
.3	.111	.07	.47	.111	.5	.47	.544	.111	.4
.07	.42	.722	.21	.722	.111	.05	.722	.63	.05
.15	.47	.24	.111	.15	.24	.111	.15	.47	.24
.544	.722	.5	.63	.722	.5	.42	.722	.5	.513
.3	.111	.722	.21	.5	.722	.544	.722	.111	.4
.513	.47	.05	.111	.07	.05	.5	.513	.47	.62
.63	.62	.5	.4	.5	.722	.24	.722	.21	.42
.544	.722	.63	.47	.722	.111	.47	.42	.111	.07
.5	.15	.05	.07	.3	.4	.62	.513	.3	.5

■ $.8$
$-.3$

◨ $.59$
$-.35$

◧ $.965$
$-.452$

◿ $.6$
$-.2$

◸ $.784$
$-.240$

■ $.314$
$-.203$

◩ $.73$
$-.31$

◪ $.79$
$-.72$

◣ $.65$
$-.44$

◿ $.78$
$-.63$

◹ $.99$
$-.37$

◿ $.94$
$-.31$

◸ $.89$
$-.84$

■ $.936$
$-.214$

◩ $.9$
$-.6$

Name_____

22.4	47.3	22.3	23.44	13.03	24.13	22.3	43.2	23.52	16.01
24.13	26.425	47.3	13.03	61.5	26.425	24.13	26.425	52.6	43.2
23.52	24.13	26.425	61.5	52.3	47.3	22.3	22.4	47.3	23.52
52.3	61.5	32.435	22.4	26.2	23.52	16.01	24.13	26.425	47.3
23.44	32.435	26.2	52.3	16.01	52.6	43.2	22.3	24.13	22.3
43.2	22.3	43.2	26.425	16.01	22.4	23.44	32.435	26.2	52.3
26.425	24.13	22.3	22.4	24.13	13.03	52.6	26.2	52.3	61.5
47.3	23.52	16.01	47.3	23.52	61.5	52.3	47.3	22.3	43.2
26.425	52.6	24.13	26.425	43.2	52.3	23.44	22.3	24.13	26.425
22.4	43.2	22.3	24.13	23.52	26.2	13.03	47.3	23.52	52.6

■
$$56.7$$
$$-34.3$$

◨
$$65.84$$
$$-52.81$$

◪
$$57.67$$
$$-34.23$$

◤
$$99.6$$
$$-52.3$$

◸
$$65.8$$
$$-43.5$$

■
$$69.24$$
$$-53.23$$

◺
$$87.8$$
$$-35.5$$

◣
$$98.9$$
$$-37.4$$

◺
$$69.9$$
$$-43.7$$

◹
$$46.89$$
$$-22.76$$

◿
$$89.678$$
$$-63.253$$

◤
$$63.5$$
$$-20.3$$

◸
$$75.83$$
$$-52.31$$

■
$$86.8$$
$$-34.2$$

◺
$$97.756$$
$$-65.321$$

11 SUBTRACTION

.092	.139	.16	.061	.269	.092	.107	.109	.061	.057
.033	.121	.750	.057	.498	.033	.389	.750	.06	.498
.109	.750	.109	.750	.269	.092	.750	.16	.750	.209
.057	.073	.750	.139	.498	.107	.061	.750	.139	.121
.750	.269	.16	.109	.389	.057	.209	.16	.092	.750
.033	.209	.109	.092	.107	.061	.06	.109	.209	.498
.057	.16	.121	.033	.389	.06	.498	.269	.16	.092
.061	.06	.073	.107	.498	.139	.073	.033	.121	.107
.16	.498	.269	.121	.057	.092	.06	.389	.033	.209
.209	.109	.073	.107	.498	.033	.061	.139	.109	.16

■ .651
−.542

◣ .907
−.638

◸ .357
−.296

◸ .305   ◹ .826   ■ .54   ◸ .643
−.184   −.793   −.38   −.586

◸ .895   ◤ .832   ◹ .741   ◹ .374
−.397   −.759   −.352   −.235

◸ .356   ◹ .624   ■ .373   ◸ .54
−.264   −.517   −.164   −.48

12 SUBTRACTION

Name_____

49.12	5.052	4.43	24.95	5.052	49.12	63.907	9.098	5.052	49.12
5.052	62.99	43.91	9.098	49.12	62.99	55.51	89.3	62.99	62.99
55.51	27.3	5.052	14.092	9.92	17.71	4.05	49.12	4.43	9.92
4.05	43.91	9.92	49.12	5.27	5.27	5.052	55.51	24.95	43.91
49.12	62.99	63.907	5.27	24.95	43.91	5.27	4.05	62.99	49.12
62.99	5.052	17.71	5.27	9.098	17.71	5.27	27.3	49.12	5.052
27.3	55.51	4.05	62.99	5.27	5.27	62.99	63.907	9.92	17.71
63.907	89.3	49.12	55.51	4.05	14.092	9.098	49.12	14.092	89.3
49.12	5.052	4.43	89.3	49.12	5.052	43.91	27.3	5.052	49.12
62.99	62.99	43.91	9.92	49.12	62.99	55.51	24.95	49.12	62.99

■ 56.35
− 7.23

◪ 15.411
− 6.313

◩ 68.876
− 4.969

◸ 94.32
−76.61

◸ 98.9
− 9.6

■ 69.35
− 6.36

◪ 29.54
−19.62

◩ 92.54
−48.63

◩ 90.428
−76.336

◹ 64.17
− 8.66

◹ 32.59
− 7.64

◹ 5.27
− .84

◸ 11.64
− 7.59

■ 12.635
− 7.583

◩ 35.6
− 8.3

13 SUBTRACTION

24.64	3.596	21.41	24.64	3.596	.64	9.03	.64	8.74	9.03
21.41	3.596	53.85	9.03	.355	21.41	7.808	81.24	7.808	8.74
24.64	81.24	21.41	9.03	9.03	48.13	44.35	9.03	48.13	53.85
3.596	9.03	9.03	3.596	21.41	7.808	33.91	21.41	24.64	8.47
3.596	.64	9.03	24.64	8.74	.355	44.35	2.86	44.35	.28
48.13	21.41	7.808	48.13	.64	8.74	.28	.33	2.86	24.64
9.03	.355	.33	2.86	8.47	2.86	24.64	53.85	48.13	3.596
81.24	.64	9.03	24.64	33.91	.33	81.24	3.596	.64	81.24
8.74	48.13	7.808	21.41	44.35	33.91	.64	48.13	21.41	7.808
9.03	8.74	.355	8.47	.28	3.596	24.64	53.85	.355	3.596

■
$$25.34$$
$$- \quad .7$$

◩
$$6.065$$
$$-5.71$$

◪
$$4.14$$
$$-3.5$$

◪
$$45.25$$
$$- \quad .9$$

◨
$$43.21$$
$$- \quad 9.3$$

■
$$4.346$$
$$- \quad .75$$

◩
$$52.03$$
$$- \quad 3.9$$

◪ $15.648 - 7.84 =$ _____

◩ $108.05 - 54.2 =$ _____

◪ $5.23 - 4.9 =$ _____

◨ $.98 - .7 =$ _____

◪ $17.87 - 9.4 =$ _____

◨ $4.16 - 1.3 =$ _____

■ $43.21 - 21.8 =$ _____

◪ $82.04 - .8 =$ _____

Name_____

4.03	10.04	29.88	.675	3.378	10.598	.031	4.03	10.04	4.03
10.04	29.88	23.175	9.45	23.175	1.288	.784	1.288	29.88	29.88
4.03	.06	2.977	.675	3.378	62.46	97.785	62.46	97.785	4.03
.675	9.45	.06	9.45	.675	.031	.784	1.288	10.598	.031
3.378	.675	2.977	23.175	3.378	62.46	1.288	10.598	.031	.784
23.175	2.977	.06	2.977	23.175	23.175	9.45	.06	3.378	23.175
10.598	97.785	10.598	.031	.784	3.378	23.175	9.45	.675	9.45
10.04	.784	1.288	.784	1.288	.675	2.977	23.175	2.977	10.04
29.88	4.03	62.46	.031	62.46	3.378	.675	9.45	4.03	29.88
4.03	10.04	29.88	.784	97.785	.06	3.378	4.03	29.88	10.04

■
$$7.4 \\ -3.37$$

◩
$$.4 \\ -.369$$

◪
$$69.4 \\ -\ 6.94$$

◤
$$.75 \\ -.075$$

◸
$$3.63 \\ -\ .252$$

■
$$11.1 \\ -\ 1.06$$

◺
$$6.32 \\ -5.032$$

◤ $23.6 - 13.002 =$ _____

◤ $1.9 - 1.116 =$ _____

◸ $23.66 - .485 =$ _____

◨ $12.3 - 2.85 =$ _____

◸ $.6 - .54 =$ _____

◸ $3.97 - .993 =$ _____

■ $38.5 - 8.62 =$ _____

◺ $98.2 - .415 =$ _____

15 SUBTRACTION

Name_____

44.5	60.1	43.2	95.5	79.52	60.1	8.79	.5	79.52	63.02
79.52	95.5	4.5	50.13	44.5	95.5	43.2	10.4	44.5	50.13
10.4	43.2	.5	8.79	.5	79.52	10.4	79.52	.5	44.5
38.42	63.02	44.5	60.1	8.79	95.5	43.2	63.02	4.5	.5
4.5	77.5	50.13	53.64	43.2	.5	7.2	38.42	77.5	10.4
.5	38.42	63.02	44.5	95.5	8.79	10.4	44.5	50.13	38.42
51.64	7.2	43.2	50.13	79.52	60.1	43.2	60.1	51.64	7.2
95.5	53.64	7.2	44.5	10.4	4.5	63.02	7.2	53.64	8.79
79.52	10.4	51.64	7.2	51.64	53.64	7.2	51.64	44.5	50.13
53.64	43.2	63.02	8.79	10.4	44.5	95.5	4.5	60.1	51.64

■ $\begin{array}{r} 54 \\ -\ \ .36 \\ \hline \end{array}$

◣ $\begin{array}{r} 96 \\ -\ \ .5 \\ \hline \end{array}$

◩ $\begin{array}{r} 39 \\ -\ \ .58 \\ \hline \end{array}$

◿ $\begin{array}{r} 9 \\ -\ .21 \\ \hline \end{array}$ ◸ $\begin{array}{r} 67 \\ -\ 6.9 \\ \hline \end{array}$ ■ $\begin{array}{r} 8 \\ -\ .8 \\ \hline \end{array}$ ◥ $\begin{array}{r} 63 \\ -52.6 \\ \hline \end{array}$

◣ 86 − 6.48 = _____   ◣ 49 − 5.8 = _____

◿ 87 − 82.5 = _____   ◿ 57 − 6.87 = _____

◿ 51 − 6.5 = _____   ◿ 23 − 22.5 = _____

■ 57 − 5.36 = _____   ◥ 64 − .98 = _____

Name_____

61.8	3.99	15.82	61.8	3.99	61.8	15.82	2.9	12.3	11.6
15.82	11.6	12.3	18.15	15.82	3.99	61.8	3.721	11.6	46.25
3.99	46.25	11.6	3.57	34.35	3.57	34.35	12.3	18.15	4.84
61.8	13.51	4.84	9.12	2.6	9.12	2.6	13.51	3.99	61.8
15.82	3.99	9.22	3.49	3.721	3.09	9.22	3.49	15.82	3.99
3.99	61.8	2.6	13.51	4.84	18.15	2.9	9.12	61.8	15.82
15.82	3.99	9.22	3.09	34.35	3.57	3.721	3.49	3.721	3.99
3.57	34.35	12.3	18.15	4.84	13.51	2.9	11.6	12.3	15.82
46.25	11.6	13.51	61.8	3.99	15.82	34.35	46.25	11.6	61.8
11.6	12.3	3.49	15.82	3.99	61.8	61.8	3.99	15.82	3.99

■ 96.3 −84 ____

◨ 6.9 −4 ____

◣ 6.57 −3 ____

◿ 45.15 −27 ____   ◸ 98.35 −64 ____   ■ 25.6 −14 ____   ◹ 25.84 −21 ____

◣ 35.49 − 32 = _____   ◹ 21.09 − 18 = _____

◿ 26.51 − 13 = _____   ◸ 29.721 − 26 = _____

◿ 68.12 − 59 = _____   ◸ 54.22 − 45 = _____

■ 98.25 − 52 = _____   ◣ 37.6 − 35 = _____

Name_____

21.7	1.3	64.38	48.025	6.92	2.33	1.2	68.64	38.2	38.4
1.2	38.4	50.31	40.4	38.4	21.7	1.3	6.92	6.1	68.64
2.33	64.38	6.1	48.025	21.7	6.1	33.46	21.7	56.75	40.4
68.64	38.2	56.75	6.66	38.4	21.7	6.66	64.38	50.31	1.2
6.92	21.7	6.1	38.4	21.7	6.1	21.7	38.4	6.1	1.3
1.2	56.75	64.38	48.025	1.2	68.64	64.38	56.75	33.46	56.75
1.3	6.92	50.31	6.66	38.2	50.31	6.66	38.2	2.33	40.4
38.4	6.1	68.64	40.4	38.4	6.1	1.3	1.2	21.7	38.4
21.7	38.4	1.3	33.46	48.025	64.38	68.64	38.2	6.1	21.7
21.7	6.1	21.7	2.33	6.92	1.3	6.92	38.4	21.7	6.1

■ 25 − 3.3 = _____   ◨ 40 − 38.8 = _____   ◸ 37 − 34.67 = _____

◺ 49 − .975 = _____   ◿ 62 − 55.08 = _____   ■ 48 − 9.6 = _____

◢ 68 − 3.62 = _____   ◣ 61 − 59.7 = _____   ◸ 58 − 7.69 = _____

◺ 74 − 5.36 = _____   ◹ 50 − 9.6 = _____   ◿ 57 − .25 = _____

◿ 39 − .8 = _____   ■ 65 − 58.9 = _____   ◸ 46 − 12.54 = _____

Name_____

71.64	70.4	.9	1.7	70.4	70.4	.342	1.7	70.4	.08
70.4	60.27	49.7	10.1	1.01	60.27	49.7	29.3	1.01	70.4
.342	6.9	.342	1.01	29.3	6.9	.9	1.01	10.1	.065
.08	.065	.08	.52	.065	60.27	1.8	71.64	.9	71.64
70.4	29.3	1.01	29.3	6.9	.08	49.7	60.27	49.7	70.4
70.4	60.27	49.7	.9	1.01	.342	1.01	.08	.065	70.4
.9	71.64	60.27	.52	49.7	10.1	.05	1.7	29.3	1.01
10.1	1.01	10.1	6.9	.9	1.7	29.3	49.7	60.27	6.9
70.4	29.3	1.7	60.27	6.9	29.3	.065	.342	49.7	70.4
.065	70.4	.08	49.7	70.4	70.4	10.1	71.64	70.4	.342

■ $\begin{array}{r} .88 \\ -.36 \\ \hline \end{array}$

◪ $\begin{array}{r} .17 \\ -.09 \\ \hline \end{array}$

◪ $\begin{array}{r} 85.036 \\ -84.026 \\ \hline \end{array}$

◤ $\begin{array}{r} 24.36 \\ -17.46 \\ \hline \end{array}$ 　　 ◸ $\begin{array}{r} 1.2 \\ -\ .3 \\ \hline \end{array}$ 　　 ■ $\begin{array}{r} 7.8 \\ -6 \\ \hline \end{array}$ 　　 ◳ $\begin{array}{r} 78.36 \\ -49.06 \\ \hline \end{array}$

◪ $8.9 - 7.2 =$ _____　　　◪ $.07 - .005 =$ _____

◤ $78 - 6.36 =$ _____　　　◸ $.6 - .258 =$ _____

◤ $54 - 4.3 =$ _____　　　◺ $68.2 - 7.93 =$ _____

■ $.9 - .85 =$ _____　　　◳ $27.5 - 17.4 =$ _____

19 MULTIPLICATION

Name_____

41.5	452.4	357.7	31.2	26.5	452.4	28.8	81.2	26.5	31.2
84.6	28.8	336.5	151.2	10.2	14.4	84.6	75.6	578.5	151.2
578.5	151.2	84.6	75.6	14.4	55.2	31.2	357.7	84.6	41.5
357.7	31.2	28.8	81.2	41.5	336.5	151.2	31.2	28.8	452.4
336.5	26.5	452.4	75.6	452.4	26.5	336.5	26.5	81.2	75.6
81.2	41.5	578.5	151.2	578.5	75.6	81.2	41.5	578.5	151.2
41.5	84.6	26.5	336.5	26.5	84.6	28.8	84.6	357.7	336.5
81.2	28.8	31.2	26.5	55.2	10.2	81.2	41.5	31.2	26.5
578.5	357.7	452.4	41.5	14.4	55.2	578.5	357.7	452.4	28.8
151.2	31.2	75.6	84.6	75.6	336.5	151.2	31.2	28.8	84.6

■ 3.4
× 3

◪ 8.3
× 5

◪ 2.8
× 29

◿ 7.8
× 4

◸ .5
×53

■ .9
×16

◩ 2.4
× 12

◪ 8.7
× 52

◣ 1.8
× 47

◿ 67.3
× 5

◿ 4.9
× 73

◿ 8.9
× 65

◸ 5.4
× 28

■ 6.9
× 8

◣ 3.6
× 21

Name_____

301.6	32.4	82.5	489.1	27.3	114	154.8	32.4	496.8	72
207.4	154.8	114	496.8	207.4	437.5	207.4	301.6	72	82.5
45.9	437.5	105.8	17.6	154.8	489.1	45.9	496.8	105.8	224
27.3	114	301.6	489.1	82.5	105.8	154.8	72	154.8	114
496.8	51.8	207.4	82.5	489.1	27.3	207.4	82.5	51.8	32.4
154.8	32.4	224	17.6	437.5	105.8	45.9	224	496.8	489.1
105.8	17.6	45.9	301.6	114	154.8	72	17.6	45.9	437.5
489.1	45.9	224	496.8	51.8	51.8	207.4	224	17.6	27.3
82.5	114	17.6	45.9	82.5	105.8	17.6	45.9	154.8	32.4
45.9	437.5	72	224	17.6	45.9	224	301.6	207.4	17.6

■ 22
× .8

◥ 60
×1.2

◥ 33
×2.5

�:

◿ 52
×5.8

◤ 46
×2.3

■ 51
× .9

◥ 20
×5.7

◣ 72
×6.9

◣ 175
× 2.5

◿ 36
×4.3

◤ 36
× .9

◿ 39
× .7

◤ 34
×6.1

■ 35
×6.4

◥ 73
×6.7

843.2	157.3	.534	12.6	.534	6.75	843.2	8.84	10.08	18.796
35.7	405.6	444.96	8.559	32.2	158.5	157.3	405.6	444.96	158.5
8.84	32.2	158.5	290.16	35.7	32.2	12.6	35.7	32.2	8.559
18.796	10.08	157.3	35.7	405.6	444.96	158.5	10.08	6.75	290.16
8.559	158.5	32.2	6.75	.534	157.3	8.559	35.7	32.2	8.84
405.6	35.7	35.7	18.796	290.16	12.6	843.2	35.7	158.5	18.796
8.84	843.2	12.6	35.7	10.08	8.84	32.2	405.6	12.6	.534
290.16	157.3	32.2	8.559	32.2	158.5	157.3	35.7	8.559	18.796
.534	444.96	158.5	290.16	158.5	35.7	444.96	158.5	843.2	157.3
12.6	35.7	8.559	6.75	405.6	18.796	10.08	6.75	35.7	405.6

■ $\begin{array}{r} 1.05 \\ \times\ 34 \\ \hline \end{array}$

◨ $\begin{array}{r} .68 \\ \times\ 13 \\ \hline \end{array}$

◧ $\begin{array}{r} 9.92 \\ \times\ 85 \\ \hline \end{array}$

◸ $\begin{array}{r} .0356 \\ \times\quad 15 \\ \hline \end{array}$
◨ $\begin{array}{r} .508 \\ \times\ 37 \\ \hline \end{array}$
■ $\begin{array}{r} .575 \\ \times\ 56 \\ \hline \end{array}$
◧ $\begin{array}{r} 6.05 \\ \times\ 26 \\ \hline \end{array}$

◧ $\begin{array}{r} 8.45 \\ \times\ 48 \\ \hline \end{array}$
◧ $\begin{array}{r} 9.36 \\ \times\ 31 \\ \hline \end{array}$
◿ $\begin{array}{r} .36 \\ \times\ 28 \\ \hline \end{array}$
◨ $\begin{array}{r} .45 \\ \times\ 28 \\ \hline \end{array}$

◸ $\begin{array}{r} .317 \\ \times\ 27 \\ \hline \end{array}$
◧ $\begin{array}{r} 9.27 \\ \times\ 48 \\ \hline \end{array}$
■ $\begin{array}{r} 6.34 \\ \times\ 25 \\ \hline \end{array}$
◧ $\begin{array}{r} .375 \\ \times\ 18 \\ \hline \end{array}$

671.8	3617.6	1009.8	671.8	36.29	36.29	671.8	3617.6	295.2	36.29
28.08	3053.7	1881	2122.9	36.29	671.8	28.08	29.92	280	1009.8
280	29.92	41.16	29.92	41.65	295.2	41.16	3053.7	1881	436.8
2122.9	671.8	36.29	671.8	280	436.8	671.8	33.29	671.8	41.65
12.48	1009.8	36.29	28.08	295.2	3617.6	295.2	36.29	28.08	52.89
52.89	29.92	41.65	436.8	41.16	29.92	1881	2122.9	280	12.48
436.8	3617.6	3053.7	28.08	295.2	41.65	2122.9	280	1009.8	41.16
671.8	41.16	1009.8	280	29.92	41.16	436.8	3617.6	29.92	671.8
36.29	36.29	280	2122.9	41.65	295.2	28.08	436.8	671.8	36.29
671.8	36.29	671.8	1881	12.48	352.8	3053.7	36.29	36.29	671.8

■ 123
×.43

◣ 125
×2.24

◤ 1020
× .99

◹ 754
×4.05

◸ 680
×5.32

■ 24
×.52

◺ 225
×8.36

◣ 598
×3.55

◣ 820
× .36

◹ 560
× .78

◸ 49
×.85

◹ 85
×.352

◸ 78
×.36

■ 144
×2.45

◺ 49
×.84

Name_____

.5768	.276	.203	.276	.154	.1368	.203	3.18	5.256	.392
3.92	.043	.232	.744	.392	5.256	.084	.744	.043	.4086
5.256	.084	.0086	.154	.028	.232	.0086	.154	3.92	.392
.028	.392	.154	.1368	.0086	.154	.1368	.154	.5768	.232
.154	.744	3.18	.1368	.302	.323	.0086	.203	.084	.0086
.1368	.5768	.4086	.1368	3.81	.083	.154	3.92	3.18	.1368
.203	.084	.1368	.0086	.154	.1368	.154	.0086	.028	.276
3.92	.276	.154	.1368	.5768	3.18	.0086	.1368	5.256	.4086
5.256	.043	.392	.203	.4086	3.92	.392	.203	.043	.392
.028	.232	.744	.084	.154	.1368	.028	.232	.744	.084

■ .77
× .2

◨ .46
× .6

◪ .35
×.08

◩ .824
× .7

◪ .58
× .4

■ .172
× .05

◪ 5.6
×.07

◪ 9.3
×.08

◪ 4.9
× .8

◪ 8.76
× .6

◪ 6.81
× .06

◩ 4.06
× .05

◩ .28
× .3

■ 4.56
× .03

◪ 6.36
× .5

Name_____

1.932	5.148	7.05	2.438	5.148	1.863	.24	2.438	.273	.0646
.24	7.05	.2646	.2829	5.148	.2646	25.604	.962	.2829	3.476
7.05	2.21	.0279	.0378	2.21	.2829	.0279	3.476	1.863	.0378
.2646	.2829	.24	7.05	2.438	3.476	7.05	1.932	.273	2.21
.0378	.0378	.2646	.2646	.24	.0646	25.604	1.932	.24	.962
3.476	2.438	1.932	.962	.273	2.438	.24	5.148	2.438	.2646
.0378	.0646	.2829	7.05	1.863	.0378	7.05	.2646	1.932	5.148
2.438	25.604	.962	.0279	.2829	.24	2.21	.2829	.24	7.05
.962	1.932	.273	1.863	5.148	2.438	.0279	.0378	7.05	2.438
25.604	1.863	.24	.2646	3.476	.2646	.24	7.05	2.21	1.932

■ 8.4
×.23

◨ 1.9
×.034

◧ 69.2
× .37

◩ 6.6
×.78

◸ 5.3
×.46

■ .69
×.41

◥ 3.7
×.26

◣ 1.05
× .26

◤ 7.9
×.44

◩ 9.6
×.025

◪ 8.5
×.26

◤ .27
×.14

◸ .42
×.63

■ .062
× .45

◥ 6.9
×.27

25 MULTIPLICATION

Name________________________

$35.08	$117.79	$49.61	$33.22	$28.99	$81.57	$32.22	$126.24	$86.66	$35.08
$86.66	$117.79	$23.22	$21.05	$86.66	$35.08	$23.22	$6.28	$35.08	$117.79
$60.75	$126.24	$60.75	$49.50	$86.66	$117.79	$49.50	$65.48	$60.75	$467.19
$33.22	$6.28	$49.50	$33.22	$35.08	$35.08	$33.22	$49.50	$106.08	$32.22
$21.05	$86.66	$117.79	$35.08	$117.79	$86.66	$35.08	$117.79	$35.08	$23.22
$126.24	$35.08	$86.66	$117.79	$35.08	$117.79	$86.66	$117.79	$86.66	$60.75
$33.22	$65.48	$49.50	$49.50	$117.79	$86.66	$33.22	$49.50	$49.61	$33.22
$81.57	$6.28	$23.22	$33.22	$86.66	$35.08	$49.50	$21.05	$81.57	$28.99
$117.79	$86.66	$60.75	$467.19	$117.79	$86.66	$60.75	$467.19	$117.79	$35.08
$35.08	$117.79	$106.08	$33.22	$65.48	$1.86	$33.22	$21.05	$35.08	$86.66

Round each answer to the nearest cent.

■ $50.12 × .7

◥ $37.13 × 3.4

◣ $15.39 × 5.3

◤ $13.78 × 3.6

◢ $87.86 × .33

■ $49.08 × 2.4

◥ $69.73 × 6.7

◣ $8.93 × 2.6

◣ $11.53 × 9.2

◤ $7.89 × 7.7

◢ $69.73 × .09

◤ $23.24 × .08

◢ $105.24 × .2

■ $12.56 × 6.9

◥ $8.97 × 7.3

.0069	.00942	.0111	.0018	.0048	.00212	.0111	.00057	.0116	.0018
.081	.02	.081	.016	.00057	.02	.019	.0164	.007	.016
.0018	.016	.007	.0111	.019	.0116	.00057	.0069	.081	.0111
.0033	.007	.0164	.081	.0069	.00057	.016	.019	.02	.0033
.00942	.0116	.00057	.0111	.0033	.0033	.0018	.0069	.081	.0164
.0018	.00513	.016	.081	.0164	.00942	.016	.019	.00513	.02
.016	.00057	.00212	.0048	.00212	.00513	.0048	.00212	.0111	.00942
.007	.0116	.007	.02	.00057	.0111	.0018	.0069	.081	.0111
.016	.00057	.016	.00942	.0164	.081	.0116	.019	.0069	.081
.00513	.0116	.0018	.0111	.007	.02	.00057	.0111	.019	.0048

■
.012
× .4

◨
.02
×.09

◧
.58
×.02

◪ .023
× .3

◩ .38
×.05

■ .0265
× .08

◧ .019
× .03

◧ .04
× .4

◧ .041
× .4

◪ .04
× .5

◪ .0157
× .6

◪ .37
×.03

◪ .09
× .9

■ .057
× .09

◧ .35
×.02

Name_____

.259	.0045	40.77	.00369	8.88	8.88	1.232	.00369	40.77	2.904
.5632	10.2	.259	10.2	7.314	.5103	10.2	.259	10.2	.333
1.232	.259	2.904	36.718	5.9928	36.718	21.654	.259	2.904	.0045
21.654	10.2	.465	.5103	.00369	.5103	7.314	5.9928	10.2	.465
8.88	5.9928	7.314	21.654	2.904	10.2	.333	40.77	36.718	8.88
8.88	40.77	.333	1.232	.259	2.904	7.314	.5632	7.314	8.88
1.232	10.2	.0045	5.9928	.465	.5632	36.718	1.232	.259	.0045
.5632	2.904	.259	7.314	1.232	.00369	40.77	2.904	10.2	.465
.5103	.259	2.904	10.2	.465	.5632	10.2	10.2	.259	7.314
10.2	.465	5.9928	.333	8.88	8.88	21.654	36.718	21.654	2.904

■ 3.63 × .8

◣ .064 × 8.8

◣ .0123 × .3

◢ 8.345 × 4.4 = _____   ◪ 45.3 × .9 = _____

■ 6.8 × 1.5 = _____   ◥ 8.02 × 2.7 = _____

◣ 1.59 × 4.6 = _____   ◣ .03 × .15 = _____

◹ 3.7 × .09 = _____   ◹ .063 × 8.1 = _____

◢ 9.3 × .05 = _____   ◤ .352 × 3.5 = _____

■ .35 × .74 = _____   ◢ .908 × 6.6 = _____

Name_____

1350	3200	90	3200	1350	90	3200	1350	3200	90
90	4750	1860	22800	10500	22800	24000	4750	10500	1350
6000	11250	16100	54600	1900	60900	16100	54600	24500	24000
16100	10500	1350	90	74000	1900	90	3200	6000	11250
6000	2070	90	3200	1900	60900	3200	1350	7200	1860
1900	74000	1900	60900	11250	16100	1900	60900	74000	1900
90	1350	6000	2070	90	3200	7200	24000	90	1350
1350	3200	24500	1900	1350	1350	1900	54600	1350	3200
22800	1860	90	1350	3200	90	3200	90	4750	10500
11250	16100	10500	3200	90	3200	1350	22800	2070	7200

■ 4500
× .3

◥ 9300
× .2

◤ 20,000
× .36

◩ 5000
× 1.2

◲ 42,000
× 1.3

■ 8000
× .4

◥ 7000
× 1.5

◣ 35,000
× .7

◣ 7000
× 2.3

◪ 19,000
× 1.2

◩ 75,000
× .15

◩ 9500
× .5

◲ 9000
× .23

■ 180
× .5

◥ 30,000
× .8

Name_____

.23	203.36	11.11	.0018	.7448	16.104	.0726	11.11	2.992	.0066
.7448	48.24	.0066	48.24	2.146	16.104	48.24	.23	1.009	.0726
1.009	2.146	16.104	1.009	1.014	.00015	1.009	2.146	16.104	1.009
203.36	48.24	11.11	.23	48.24	25.2	.0066	48.24	11.11	1.014
.0066	.00015	2.992	11.11	1.009	11.11	12.528	203.36	2.992	2.992
.0726	56.595	.0018	21.6	48.24	1.009	48.24	56.595	2.146	.0018
16.104	48.24	11.11	2.146	25.2	11.11	16.104	1.009	11.11	.7448
1.009	.23	203.36	48.24	.7448	.0726	48.24	.23	.00015	48.24
1.014	1.009	16.104	1.009	1.014	.0066	11.11	2.146	1.009	.0066
2.146	56.595	11.11	2.992	.23	.0066	203.36	48.24	.0018	16.104

■
$$2.8 \times 9$$

◤
$$5.32 \times .14$$

◣
$$.0005 \times .3$$

◥
$$3.3 \times .022$$

◤
$$6.8 \times .44$$

■
$$34.8 \times .36$$

◤
$$.37 \times 5.8$$

◣
$$12.4 \times 16.4$$

◣
$$.132 \times .05$$

◥
$$7.35 \times 7.7$$

◤
$$16.9 \times .06$$

◥ $6.71 \times 2.4 =$ _____

◤ $4.6 \times .05 =$ _____

■ $54 \times .4 =$ _____

◣ $.06 \times .03 =$ _____

Name_____

123.6	3.57	92.8	3.57	53.7	.18	92.8	3.57	92.8	12.8
3.57	.32	.82	.904	.32	.82	.904	.32	.904	3.57
92.8	.82	4.69	3.36	4.69	.54	8.1	.54	.82	3.57
3.57	.904	4.261	.904	123.6	12.8	.32	32.6	.32	92.8
3.2	.32	53.7	3.36	3.2	.18	8.1	20.6	.904	20.6
12.8	.82	8.1	20.6	32.6	4.261	4.69	123.6	.82	123.6
92.8	.32	.18	.32	.54	53.7	.82	3.2	.32	3.57
3.57	.904	32.6	20.6	12.8	3.36	4.69	3.36	.904	3.57
3.57	.82	.32	.904	.82	.32	.904	.82	.32	92.8
.54	3.57	92.8	3.57	12.8	4.261	92.8	92.8	3.57	53.7

■ $7\overline{)2.24}$

◨ $9\overline{)115.2}$

◪ $3\overline{).54}$

◸ $3\overline{)370.8}$ ◪ $6\overline{)322.2}$ ■ $6\overline{)4.92}$ ◧ $5\overline{)40.5}$

◥ $7\overline{)3.78}$ ◣ $4\overline{)82.4}$ ◿ $9\overline{)30.24}$ ◪ $8\overline{)25.6}$

◿ $8\overline{)34.088}$ ◿ $7\overline{)32.83}$ ■ $4\overline{)3.616}$ ◧ $9\overline{)293.4}$

.35	3.15	5.46	.525	1.155	5.25	.425	.365	.465	2.92
.925	.425	.315	.35	.36	.12	2.92	.315	.36	.65
.525	5.32	.65	3.15	6.24	5.32	.65	5.25	6.24	.12
.65	.525	6.24	5.32	5.46	.36	6.24	5.36	5.46	.925
.425	.35	5.36	.425	.315	.35	.365	5.32	2.92	.525
1.155	2.92	6.24	5.32	2.92	2.92	5.36	6.24	.315	3.15
.525	.465	.525	.65	.35	.315	3.15	5.46	.925	.12
.35	.36	1.155	.525	1.155	5.25	.425	5.25	.425	.35
.315	2.92	.525	.65	.525	.12	3.15	5.46	.315	2.92
2.92	.35	2.92	.365	.465	.925	.425	.35	2.92	.35

■ $8\overline{)2.8}$

◣ $4\overline{)1.86}$

◣ $8\overline{)2.92}$

◹ $6\overline{)31.5}$ ◸ $5\overline{).6}$ ■ $5\overline{)14.6}$ ◣ $8\overline{)5.2}$

◺ $8\overline{)4.2}$ ◣ $5\overline{)1.8}$ ◹ $4\overline{)3.7}$ ◸ $5\overline{)27.3}$

◹ $6\overline{)18.9}$ ◸ $6\overline{)2.55}$ ■ $4\overline{)1.26}$ ◣ $6\overline{)6.93}$

Name_____

.021	.00641	.0542	.0417	.042	.55	.097	.012	.0073	.0347
.099	.055	.0037	.0012	.0347	.021	.0083	.012	.034	.0524
.0542	.55	.042	.024	.0083	.0012	.024	.0037	.042	.55
.006	.024	.0083	.0012	.0524	.099	.0012	.0083	.024	.0036
.036	.034	.0012	.055	.021	.0417	.006	.0012	.0036	.06
.0714	.097	.0083	.00641	.099	.0524	.097	.0083	.0347	.036
.0073	.024	.0083	.0012	.0417	.021	.0012	.0083	.024	.00641
.0714	.0542	.55	.024	.0083	.0012	.024	.042	.012	.06
.097	.0347	.036	.024	.055	.006	.024	.012	.0073	.0417
.034	.055	.0714	.0524	.036	.042	.099	.55	.006	.0036

■ 3)‾.072‾

◩ 7)‾.042‾

■ 3)‾.1041‾

◩ 5)‾.275‾   ◩ 4)‾.0292‾   ■ 6)‾.0498‾   ◩ 9)‾.306‾

◩ 8)‾.3336‾   ◩ 6)‾.03846‾   ◩ 7)‾.0252‾   ◩ 3)‾.291‾

◩ 9)‾.4716‾   ◩ 8)‾.168‾   ■ 4)‾.0048‾   ◩ 5)‾.495‾

3.2	.75	121	6	1.2	12.86	7.5	3.26	.75	3.2
32.6	8.1	32	9	2.1	.81	7.8	6	307.2	32.6
8.1	7.5	2	8	6	7.5	307.2	7.3	32	3.26
6	2	121	7.5	9	7.3	7.5	98	12.86	32
1.2	.81	32	9	8	3.26	7.8	6	3.2	7.3
307.2	1.286	7.5	98	12.86	1.2	8.1	32	1.286	8
6	307.2	7.8	7.5	3.26	121	32	2	8.1	6
7.3	32	98	7.8	7.5	32	1.2	8	6	9
.75	12.86	32	3.26	1.21	32.6	8.1	7.5	2	128.6
.81	3.2	7.8	6	98	121	32	1.2	.78	30.72

■ $.2\overline{)6.4}$

◪ $.05\overline{).1}$

◩ $.8\overline{)78.4}$

� ◩ $.007\overline{).0511}$ ◪ $.006\overline{).048}$ ■ $.05\overline{).375}$ ◨ $.09\overline{).702}$

■ $.003\overline{).9216}$ ◨ $.04\overline{).1304}$ ◪ $.7\overline{)6.3}$ ◪ $.9\overline{)7.29}$

◪ $.004\overline{).0048}$ ◪ $.03\overline{)3.63}$ ■ $.6\overline{)3.6}$ ◨ $.8\overline{)10.288}$

230	960	90	7700	4320	4950	3610	245	640	710
370	385	330	9600	230	3610	4950	710	7700	960
385	640	4320	330	9600	370	3610	4950	960	230
640	710	4230	370	385	7700	4320	90	330	9600
230	960	245	7700	4320	4950	3610	4230	640	710
370	385	90	4950	3610	330	9600	245	230	960
7700	4320	4230	330	9600	640	710	90	370	385
960	230	3610	4950	710	7700	4320	330	385	640
230	9600	370	3610	4950	960	7700	4320	640	710
370	385	245	4950	3610	330	9600	4230	230	960

■ $.02 \overline{)84.6}$

◨ $.08 \overline{)30.8}$

◨ $.07 \overline{)25.9}$

◰ $.0002 \overline{).066}$ ◰ $.006 \overline{)57.6}$ ◨ $.0007 \overline{).497}$ ■ $.06 \overline{)14.7}$

◨ $.05 \overline{)247.5}$ ◨ $.009 \overline{)5.76}$ ◰ $.007 \overline{)53.9}$ ◰ $.01 \overline{)9.6}$

◰ $.03 \overline{)6.9}$ ◨ $.004 \overline{)14.44}$ ◰ $.008 \overline{)34.56}$ ■ $.09 \overline{)8.1}$

Name _____

5.625	191.25	164.5	.485	3.375	191.25	24.05	1.78	5.625	191.25
191.4	3.24	.695	.26	112.5	24.05	.695	.26	3.24	.485
45.5	164.5	.45	3.24	3.375	45.5	.45	.45	1.78	3.375
1.78	.26	3.24	.45	191.4	1.78	3.24	.45	.695	164.5
3.375	.485	.26	191.25	.185	8.75	5.625	.695	191.4	191.25
24.05	.695	164.5	.485	8.75	.65	164.5	.485	.26	112.5
45.5	191.4	.45	3.24	.26	45.5	3.24	.45	.485	3.375
1.78	5.625	3.24	.45	24.05	1.78	3.24	.45	191.25	164.5
.26	.45	.485	191.4	.695	3.375	.485	191.4	3.24	.695
24.05	112.5	3.375	.695	164.5	112.5	.26	191.25	24.05	1.78

◰ .05)‾.013

◲ .04)‾7.65

◱ .05)‾9.57

◰ .008)‾.045   ◪ .2)‾.097   ■ .04)‾.35   ◱ .4)‾.278

◣ .2)‾4.81   ◰ .005)‾.0089   ◰ .008)‾.027   ◱ .6)‾98.7

■ .02)‾.0037   ◰ .06)‾6.75   ■ .006)‾.0039   ◱ .08)‾3.64

.067	.093	.093	.029	.0265	.059	.097	.093	.093	.0046
.0786	.0294	.0148	.0069	.0148	.0294	.00752	.067	.0148	.0245
.048	.0097	.059	.067	.0068	.0069	.0148	.0097	.00752	.048
.0069	.0046	.097	.0068	.0294	.029	.0069	.029	.067	.059
.0148	.0265	.00752	.067	.00752	.0265	.0148	.0265	.00752	.0294
.0068	.0294	.0148	.0069	.029	.067	.059	.097	.029	.0069
.0294	.059	.0097	.0148	.0069	.0068	.097	.0068	.0097	.0148
.0245	.067	.0046	.0097	.0046	.067	.00752	.0294	.0046	.0245
.048	.0265	.00752	.067	.059	.0097	.029	.0265	.00752	.0786
.0069	.093	.093	.059	.097	.0148	.0069	.093	.093	.059

■ .3$\overline{).02358}$

◪ .09$\overline{).00531}$

◪ .3$\overline{).0291}$

◪ .04$\overline{).00106}$ ◪ .2$\overline{).00092}$ ◪ .06$\overline{).0004512}$ ■ .6$\overline{).0288}$

◪ .03$\overline{).000444}$ ◪ .08$\overline{).002352}$ ◪ .09$\overline{).000873}$ ◪ .07$\overline{).00469}$

◪ .4$\overline{).00276}$ ◪ .7$\overline{).0203}$ ■ .02$\overline{).00049}$ ◪ .5$\overline{).0034}$

Name_____

98	3400	520	2400	2300	5900	60	3380	2320	80
230	2300	90	460	230	2320	3400	460	5900	78
60	230	2300	2400	60	5900	2300	3380	78	2400
460	3380	78	40	3400	460	80	90	520	230
2300	3400	520	80	3380	60	40	5900	2320	5900
78	5900	2320	98	230	78	98	230	2300	90
520	230	60	40	2400	520	80	3380	78	2400
2320	5900	78	90	2320	230	460	3400	60	3400
3380	78	2400	2300	3380	2300	5900	520	90	2300
40	2400	460	3400	78	90	460	230	60	98

■ .5)49

� .3)696

◢ .2)676

◺ .02)68   ◤ .9)54   ■ .6)24   ◣ .5)39

◣ .06)144   ◣ .03)177   ◺ .7)63   ◺ .4)208

◺ .4)92   ◤ .08)184   ■ .8)64   ◱ .2)92

Name_____

3.9	13.9	9.8	39.4	9.8	6.46	4.8	3.76	6.8	26.2
62.5	6.46	3.76	12.3	63.9	79.3	63.9	6.46	3.9	9.4
3.76	79.3	26.2	6.46	4.8	12.3	4.8	3.9	26.2	29.7
69.3	6.1	3.9	26.2	6.1	3.9	63.9	4.8	63.9	4.8
13.9	63.9	4.8	12.3	6.46	26.2	3.9	69.3	62.5	26.2
3.9	29.7	6.8	26.2	3.9	6.46	39.4	4.8	63.9	79.3
63.9	4.8	63.9	4.8	26.2	9.4	26.2	3.9	69.3	6.8
62.5	26.2	3.9	63.9	69.3	4.8	6.46	26.2	29.7	9.8
6.1	6.46	26.2	4.8	3.76	63.9	39.4	9.8	3.9	13.9
3.9	9.4	79.3	4.8	6.46	13.9	12.3	29.7	62.5	6.46

■ 34)890.8

◣ 68)666.4

◣ 18)67.68

◲ 18)709.2   ◪ 27)183.6   ◳ 37)2312.5   ■ 26)101.4

◣ 69)959.1   ◣ 33)980.1   ◱ 63)592.2   ◩ 72)439.2

◪ 38)2633.4   ◳ 28)2220.4   ■ 54)348.84   ◩ 49)602.7

6.18	3.65	.238	3.65	6.44	6.44	.246	.486	.246	6.18
8.15	3.45	9.55	.238	9.55	3.75	.486	3.75	6.18	2.85
.328	7.65	3.666	.328	8.15	9.35	8.65	6.18	9.35	8.65
7.65	9.55	8.15	6.18	3.65	.246	3.45	2.85	3.75	.486
6.44	.238	3.65	.238	3.45	3.666	.486	.246	9.35	6.44
6.44	.246	9.35	3.75	6.18	3.45	3.65	7.65	9.55	6.44
8.65	2.85	.246	3.45	2.85	7.65	3.666	.328	.238	.328
.486	.246	3.666	9.35	8.65	9.55	8.15	6.18	3.65	.238
3.75	3.45	9.35	3.75	.486	7.65	.328	8.15	3.45	9.55
6.18	2.85	8.65	2.85	6.44	6.44	8.15	.328	7.65	3.666

■ $85\overline{)525.3}$

◣ $45\overline{)10.71}$

◪ $58\overline{)211.7}$

◺ $95\overline{)46.17}$　◪ $85\overline{)20.91}$　■ $34\overline{)117.3}$　◹ $56\overline{)456.4}$

◣ $75\overline{)24.6}$　◥ $72\overline{)687.6}$　◺ $26\overline{)74.1}$　◸ $62\overline{)232.5}$

◺ $38\overline{)355.3}$　◩ $34\overline{)294.1}$　■ $35\overline{)128.31}$　◣ $78\overline{)596.7}$

Name_____

.082	.09	.086	.034	.09	.0068	.0098	.094	.0068	.09
.0068	.082	.062	.04	.082	.09	.027	.06	.082	.0068
.082	.09	.08	.088	.09	.0068	.08	.094	.0068	.09
.082	.0068	.078	.062	.082	.0068	.078	.057	.082	.0068
.09	.082	.088	.086	.082	.09	.034	.0098	.0068	.09
.0068	.09	.04	.062	.08	.094	.06	.027	.082	.0068
.082	.086	.0068	.0098	.057	.04	.034	.09	.094	.09
.09	.04	.034	.06	.027	.078	.027	.0098	.057	.082
.0068	.082	.06	.088	.086	.034	.08	.027	.082	.0068
.082	.09	.0068	.078	.027	.04	.062	.09	.0068	.09

■ $64\overline{)5.76}$

◥ $67\overline{)6.298}$

◣ $26\overline{)1.56}$

◿ $51\overline{)4.386}$ ◸ $57\overline{)3.534}$ ■ $37\overline{).2516}$ ◥ $72\overline{)2.448}$

◣ $64\overline{)2.56}$ ◤ $48\overline{)3.744}$ ◿ $19\overline{)1.52}$ ◸ $76\overline{)4.332}$

◿ $72\overline{).7056}$ ◸ $38\overline{)1.026}$ ■ $33\overline{)2.706}$ ◥ $29\overline{)2.552}$

41 DIVISION

Name ____________________

87.3	75.3	.25	8.32	7.46	75.3	.25	75.3	7.46	5.96
6.5	7.82	6.5	9.37	8.32	9.37	8.32	9.37	6.57	9.37
730	75.3	6.57	6.5	7.46	6.5	.25	6.9	7.46	4.86
8.32	40	75.3	6.9	75.3	.25	7.82	7.46	780	.25
40	8.32	5.96	8.32	4.86	730	9.37	87.3	9.37	87.3
6.5	730	6.5	730	7.46	8.32	4.86	7.46	4.86	.25
5.96	75.3	5.96	6.57	40	780	7.82	780	.25	780
8.32	40	7.82	40	87.3	5.96	87.3	6.9	87.3	9.37
40	6.9	730	780	730	4.86	730	4.86	6.57	87.3
.25	730	4.86	5.96	780	5.96	87.3	40	780	75.3

■ 3.4)26.588

◪ 8.4)50.064

◪ .058).0145

◩ .94)82.062 ◪ 6.8)512.04 ■ .64)4.2048 ◪ .78)569.4

◪ 6.2)46.252 ◪ .89)8.3393 ◩ .024)18.72 ◪ 9.7)80.704

◩ .39)1.8954 ◪ 4.7)30.55 ■ .79)5.451 ◪ .0052).208

Name_____

.037	.0068	.0094	.03	.0334	.0375	.0097	.092	.063	.0447
.046	.0097	.0447	.086	.092	.016	.037	.0447	.03	.006
.04	.0094	.037	.0447	.037	.086	.037	.086	.04	.0094
.0447	.086	.0375	.006	.086	.0447	.0068	.063	.0447	.0447
.037	.086	.03	.0097	.086	.037	.092	.016	.0447	.086
.063	.0447	.037	.0068	.037	.0447	.006	.086	.037	.0068
.0759	.0334	.046	.0097	.0447	.086	.092	.0334	.046	.0759
.04	.0759	.0759	.006	.0375	.063	.0068	.0759	.0759	.016
.0447	.03	.016	.092	.0097	.03	.0094	.04	.0097	.0447
.063	.086	.0375	.0334	.046	.0334	.0068	.006	.086	.046

■ 4.9)‾.21903‾

◩ .78)‾.04914‾

■ .6)‾.0516‾

◪ .13)‾.004875‾   ◪ .57)‾.005358‾   ■ .069)‾.002553‾   ◲ 4.3)‾.0258‾

◣ .53)‾.04876‾   ◣ 6.5)‾.195‾   ◤ .84)‾.005712‾   ◩ 3.6)‾.0576‾

◤ 6.2)‾.2852‾   ◥ 4.9)‾.04753‾   ◣ .026)‾.00104‾   ◳ 2.9)‾.09686‾

43 DIVISION

$2.12	$1.22	$3.30	$2.12	$47.71	$2.31	$2.12	$3.30	$1.22	$2.12
$47.71	$2.31	$1.22	$0.69	$0.96	$7.23	$3.29	$1.22	$0.69	$9.61
$2.04	$1.41	$3.30	$20.87	$3.29	$0.88	$275.90	$3.30	$7.23	$1.41
$2.12	$1.22	$47.71	$9.61	$7.23	$0.96	$0.88	$3.29	$1.22	$3.30
$3.30	$0.69	$1.41	$20.87	$2.31	$0.69	$275.90	$20.87	$9.61	$2.12
$1.22	$2.04	$9.61	$0.69	$0.96	$7.23	$2.31	$0.69	$1.41	$1.22
$1.22	$3.30	$20.87	$275.90	$0.88	$3.29	$20.87	$275.90	$2.12	$3.30
$0.88	$2.31	$2.12	$47.71	$0.96	$7.23	$9.61	$1.22	$0.88	$9.61
$7.23	$1.41	$3.30	$2.04	$9.61	$47.71	$0.96	$3.30	$7.23	$275.90
$1.22	$2.12	$1.22	$3.30	$20.87	$1.41	$1.22	$2.12	$1.22	$3.30

Round each answer to the nearest cent.

■ 23) $48.87

◩ 32) $73.86

◪ 34) $69.24

◿ 7) $4.84   ◹ 7) $9.84   ■ 76) $92.47   ◧ 15) $49.36

◪ 11) $79.52   ◩ 8) $166.94   ◸ 6) $5.30   ◿ 4) $3.83

◿ 2.7) $128.83   ◹ 3) $827.69   ■ 27) $88.97   ◩ 4) $38.42

Name_____

678	9	91	46	91	11.8	37	11.8	43	94
.25	64	23	91	1.17	64	11.8	77	1.17	150
37	.008	150	46	11.8	91	37	.25	.0064	46
150	1.17	77	9	11.8	91	150	46	37	9
1.17	.0064	.25	91	.25	.0064	11.8	43	.008	37
.0043	91	11.8	.008	64	46	43	11.8	91	94
.008	64	.25	37	.0043	678	1.17	43	23	.0064
37	9	11.8	150	.25	43	.008	91	150	46
43	23	64	46	37	1.17	77	46	64	9
91	.0064	.008	43	9	150	.25	.0064	.008	11.8

◪ $7\overline{).056}$

◩ $.07\overline{)3.01}$

◣ $3.8\overline{)174.8}$

◨ $.6\overline{)5.4}$　　◪ $.005\overline{).185}$　　◼ $.007\overline{).658}$　　◩ $6\overline{).0384}$

◢ $.09\overline{)2.07}$　　◣ $8.8\overline{)10.296}$　　◼ $.078\overline{)52.884}$　　◪ $9.4\overline{)601.6}$

◪ $.36\overline{).09}$　　◪ $.04\overline{)3.08}$　　◼ $62\overline{).2666}$　　◩ $.008\overline{)1.2}$

45 MIXED REVIEW

Name_____

23.8	10.9	129.05	5.71	69.6	93.5	51.11	97.9	46.9	30.69
66.2	46.9	63.24	51.11	97.9	23.8	10.9	69.6	63.24	23.8
69.6	30.69	10.9	129.05	30.69	89.53	97.9	84	10.9	129.05
84	23.8	46.9	63.24	129.05	63.24	.51	66.2	46.9	30.69
23.8	10.9	.51	66.2	69.6	97.9	23.8	51.11	63.24	84
89.53	5.71	84	51.11	5.71	51.11	5.71	10.9	10.9	89.53
63.24	51.11	66.2	89.53	93.5	89.53	93.5	84	23.8	69.6
46.9	66.2	69.6	63.24	129.05	63.24	23.8	46.9	66.2	10.9
93.5	51.11	97.9	84	51.11	5.71	129.05	30.69	69.6	97.9
84	46.9	30.69	10.9	23.8	.51	93.5	84	10.9	.51

■ 76.8
   + 7.2

◩ 70
   − 3.8

◩ 64.3
   + 5.3

◨ 83.12
   +45.93

◪ 79.38
   −48.69

■ 67.8
   −56.9

◩ .87
   −.36

◧ 94.78
   −43.67

◪ 87.6
   + 5.9

■ 73.5
   −49.7

◩ 37.8
   −32.09

◧ 67.9 + 30 = _____

◪ 98 − 8.47 = _____

◪ 29.9 + 17 = _____

◪ 64.8 − 1.56 = _____

Name_____

.005	21.16	244.8	8.79	.008	92.7	8.79	.007	21.16	.005
27.648	.005	280.44	3.08	8.79	.008	.056	5.13	.005	27.648
.32	.007	21.16	27.648	92.7	.008	27.648	21.16	635.68	.018
92.7	28.12	27.648	.005	28.12	.056	21.16	.005	1.702	8.79
8.79	.008	8.79	5.13	244.8	.005	1.702	8.79	.008	92.7
92.7	8.79	.008	1.43	21.16	28.12	244.8	8.79	92.7	8.79
8.79	.007	.005	.005	.018	.32	.005	21.16	635.68	.008
1.702	3.08	27.648	21.16	8.79	92.7	27.648	.005	280.44	3.08
27.648	.005	244.8	.018	.008	8.79	244.8	1.43	21.16	.005
21.16	27.648	.056	8.79	92.7	.008	8.79	28.12	.005	27.648

◨ $25\overline{)\,.175}$

◨ $64\overline{)\,1.152}$

◨ $38\overline{)\,2.128}$

◩ 6.8
× 36

◤ 77
×.04

◼ 7.68
× 3.6

◨ 3.7
×.46

◨ 73.8
× 3.8

◼ 3.68
×5.75

◿ 13.7
×46.4

◸ 7.4
×3.8

◿ $6.7\overline{)\,2.144}$ ◤ $16\overline{)\,82.08}$ ◼ $6.7\overline{)\,.0335}$ ◨ $5.3\overline{)\,7.579}$

3.7	28.5	$38.94	$5.80	3.7	123.4	121.2	28	.043	28.5
121.2	$2.84	123.4	.043	$1.20	$2.84	28.5	3.7	$2.84	$5.80
28.5	$38.94	$1.20	28	121.2	28	$38.94	$1.20	28	.043
$5.80	.043	$5.80	$1.20	.043	123.4	$2.84	121.2	123.4	$38.94
3.7	$2.84	123.4	3.7	28	121.2	28.5	3.7	$1.20	28.5
121.2	$1.20	$5.80	121.2	28.5	3.7	$5.80	$38.94	$2.84	28
28.5	$38.94	28.5	$1.20	$38.94	28	$2.84	.043	$5.80	3.7
$5.80	3.7	$2.84	123.4	.043	28.5	3.7	$1.20	28.5	$38.94
.043	$1.20	$5.80	121.2	$2.84	$1.20	$5.80	$38.94	$2.84	123.4
$38.94	28	3.7	123.4	$38.94	28	.043	123.4	121.2	28

Bought 4 apples at $0.30 each. What was the total cost?

4 decks of cards. $1.45 a deck. Total cost?

Total cost of 6 TV dinners was $17.04. How much for 1?

Made 7 liters of jam. Each jar held 0.25 liter. How many jars were needed?

Find my number. It is 0.05 times the number 0.86. What is the number?

3 dresses. $12.98 a dress. Total cost?

Sally's time in the first lap of a race was 63.8 seconds. Her time in the second lap was 59.6 seconds. What was her total time in seconds for the two laps?

Bob's fever dropped from 102.3° to 98.6°. How many degrees did it drop?

The odometer of a car read 1048.6 at the start of a trip. At the end it read 1169.8. How far did the car travel?

The morning low temperature was 69.8° F. The afternoon high temperature was 98.3° F. By how much did the high and low differ?

Name_____

2213.7	14.98	$15.92	4.6	$0.51	$0.32	$0.51	4.6	$8.72	2213.7
14.8	$4.65	14.8	.38	$15.92	4.6	.38	$8.72	$4.65	.44
$0.51	14.98	2213.7	14.98	$15.92	$0.32	.44	2213.7	.44	$0.32
.44	.38	14.8	$4.65	14.8	$8.72	$4.65	$8.72	.38	14.8
$0.51	$15.92	$0.51	14.98	$15.92	4.6	.44	4.6	$0.32	4.6
$8.72	.44	$8.72	$0.32	.44	14.8	$15.92	14.8	14.98	14.8
$15.92	.38	4.6	2213.7	4.6	$0.51	2213.7	$15.92	.38	$0.32
.44	$0.32	$4.65	$0.32	.44	14.98	$0.51	$4.65	$0.51	14.98
4.6	2213.7	4.6	.38	$8.72	14.8	.38	$15.92	2213.7	$15.92
$4.65	$0.32	$8.72	14.8	.44	14.98	$8.72	14.8	$0.51	$4.65

◨ Bought 4 pies at $3.98 each. Total cost?

◨ $6.12 for a dozen donuts. How much for 1?

◼ Had a $10.00 bill. Spent $5.35. How much was left?

◨ A length of 0.53 cm is cut from a 0.97 cm length of wire. How much wire is left?

◨ Find my number. It is 8.9 more than 6.08. What is my number?

◨ Alice's temperature went from 98.6° F to 103.2° F. How many degrees did it increase?

◼ The odometer read 2489.6 at the end of a trip. If the trip was 275.9 miles, what was the reading at the start of the trip?

◨ Eight pairs of socks were bought. The cost was $1.09 a pair. What was the total cost?

◨ A car used 8.6 gallons of fuel on one trip. On another trip it used 6.2 gallons. What was the total amount used on both trips?

◼ Nancy bought an $8.00 item. The sales tax rate was $0.04 per dollar. How much tax was added to the $8.00?

SOLUTION KEY

1 ADDITION

.65

8.6

7.77

6.705	6.886	5.79	9.97
8.97	8.89	7.729	9.9
7.67	9.99	5.876	7.98

2 ADDITION

9.43

69.6

113.1

82.7	111.3	.35	1.4
.37	128.21	.824	49.629
22.2	.17	.85	104.4

3 ADDITION

55.2

408

1.339

1.3	82.7
14.6	74.82
85.3	413
87.6	85.02
69.6	139.73
81.3	161.41

4 ADDITION

1.033

.49

5.122

44.103	14.55	93.99	.908
85.22	.86	43.34	37.83
43.74	14.05	1.66	7.34

5 ADDITION

186.95

86.95

41.06

.65	78.14
.95	36.96
35.1	17.59
1.274	7.365
43.18	440.61
55.12	61.73

6 ADDITION

90.4

9.42

47.7

40.2	35.87	39.2
17.47	90.26	3.35
97.25	23.8	20.52
26.9	9.871	25.4

7 ADDITION

28.814

54.39

6.34

21.27	88.88	64.55	50.7
	54.55		100.13
	12.63		1.52
	24.94		36.43
	34.15		23.42

8 REVIEW

89.42

85.09

23.63

7.151	27.43	21.32	99.23
	3.3		1.7
	7.78		17.42
	8.42		1.027
	16.66		18.34

9 SUBTRACTION

.5

.24

.513

.4	.544	.111	.42
.07	.21	.15	.62
.63	.05	.722	.3

10 SUBTRACTION

22.4

13.03

23.44

47.3	22.3	16.01	52.3
61.5	26.2	24.13	26.425
43.2	23.52	52.6	32.435

11 SUBTRACTION

.109

.269

.061

.121	.033	.16	.057
.498	.073	.389	.139
.092	.107	.209	.06

12 SUBTRACTION

49.12

9.098

63.907

17.71	89.3	62.99	9.92
43.91	14.092	55.51	24.95
4.43	4.05	5.052	27.3

13 SUBTRACTION

24.64

.355

.64

44.35	33.91	3.596	48.13
	7.808		53.85
	.33		.28
	8.47		2.86
	21.41		81.24

14 SUBTRACTION

4.03

.031

62.46

.675	3.378	10.04	1.288
	10.598		.784
	23.175		9.45
	.06		2.977
	29.88		97.785

15 SUBTRACTION

53.64

95.5

38.42

8.79	60.1	7.2	10.4
	79.52		43.2
	4.5		50.13
	44.5		.5
	51.64		63.02

16 SUBTRACTION

12.3

2.9

3.57

18.15	34.35	11.6	4.84
	3.49		3.09
	13.51		3.721
	9.12		9.22
	46.25		2.6

17 SUBTRACTION

21.7	1.2	2.33
48.025	6.92	38.4
64.38	1.3	50.31
68.64	40.4	56.75
38.2	6.1	33.46

18 REVIEW

.52

.08

1.01

6.9	.9	1.8	29.3
	1.7		.065
	71.64		.342
	49.7		60.27
	.05		10.1

19 MULTIPLICATION

10.2

41.5

81.2

31.2	26.5	14.4	28.8
452.4	84.6	336.5	357.7
578.5	151.2	55.2	75.6

20 MULTIPLICATION

17.6

72

82.5

301.6	105.8	45.9	114
496.8	437.5	154.8	324
27.3	207.4	224	489.1

21 MULTIPLICATION

35.7

8.84

843.2

.534	18.796	32.2	157.3
405.6	290.16	10.08	12.6
8.559	444.96	158.5	6.75

22 MULTIPLICATION

52.89

280

1009.8

3053.7	3617.6	12.48	1881
2122.9	295.2	436.8	41.65
29.92	28.08	352.8	41.16

23 MULTIPLICATION

.154

.276

.028

.5768	.232	.0086	.392
.744	3.92	5.256	.4086
.203	.084	.1368	3.18

24 MULTIPLICATION

1.932

.0646

25.604

5.148	2.438	.2829	.962
.273	3.476	.24	2.21
.0378	.2646	.0279	1.863

25 MULTIPLICATION

$35.08

$126.24

$81.57

$49.61	$28.99	$117.79	$467.19
$23.22	$106.08	$60.75	$6.28
$1.86	$21.05	$86.66	$65.48

26 MULTIPLICATION

.0048

.0018

.0116

.0069	.019	.00212	.00057
.016	.0164	.02	.00942
.0111	.081	.00513	.007

27 MULTIPLICATION

2.904

.5632

.00369

36.718	40.77
10.2	21.654
7.314	.0045
.333	.5103
.465	1.232
.259	5.9928

28 MULTIPLICATION

1350

1860

7200

6000	54,600	3200	10,500
24,500	16,100	22,800	11,250
4750	2070	90	24,000

29 REVIEW

25.2

.7448

.00015

.0726	2992	12.528	2.146
203.36	.0066	56.595	1.014
	16.104		.23
	21.6		.0018

30 DIVISION

.32

12.8

.18

123.6	53.7	.82	8.1
.54	20.6	3.36	3.2
4.261	4.69	.904	32.6

31 DIVISION

.35

.465

.365

5.25	.12	2.92	.65
.525	.36	.925	5.46
3.15	.425	.315	1.155

32 DIVISION

.024

.006

.0347

.055	.0073	.0083	.034
.0417	.00641	.0036	.097
.0524	.021	.0012	.099

33 DIVISION

32

2

98

7.3	8	7.5	7.8
307.2	3.26	9	8.1
1.2	121	6	12.86

34 DIVISION

4230

385

370

330	9600	710	245
4950	640	7700	960
230	3610	4320	90

35 DIVISION

.26

191.25

191.4

5.625	.485	8.75	.695
24.05	1.78	3.375	164.5
.185	112.5	.65	45.5

36 DIVISION

.0786

.059

.097

.0265	.0046	.00752	.048
.0148	.0294	.0097	.067
.0069	.029	.0245	.0068

37 DIVISION

98
2320
3380

3400	60	40	78
2400	5900	90	520
230	2300	80	460

38 DIVISION

26.2
9.8
3.76

39.4	6.8	62.5	3.9
13.9	29.7	9.4	6.1
69.3	79.3	6.46	12.3

39 DIVISION

6.18
.238
3.65

.486	.246	3.45	8.15
.328	9.55	2.85	3.75
9.35	8.65	3.666	7.65

40 DIVISION

.09
.094
.06

.086	.062	.0068	.034
.04	.078	.08	.057
.0098	.027	.082	.088

41 DIVISION

7.82
5.96
.25

87.3	75.3	6.57	730
7.46	9.37	780	8.32
4.86	6.5	6.9	40

42 DIVISION

.0447
.063
.086

.0375	.0094	.037	.006
.092	.03	.0068	.016
.046	.0097	.04	.0334

43 DIVISION

$2.12
$2.31
$2.04

$0.69	$1.41	$1.22	$3.29
$7.23	$20.87	$0.88	$0.96
$47.71	$275.90	$3.30	$9.61

44 REVIEW

.008
43
46

9	37	94	.0064
23	1.17	678	64
.25	77	.0043	150

45 MIXED REVIEW

84
66.2
69.6

129.05	30.69	10.9	51
51.11	93.5	23.8	5.71
	97.9		89.53
	46.9		63.24

46 MIXED REVIEW

.007
.018
.056

244.8	3.08	27.648	1.702
280.44	21.16	635.68	28.12
.32	5.13	.005	1.43

47 WORD PROBLEMS

$1.20
$5.80

$2.84	28
.043	$38.94
123.4	3.7
121.2	28.5

48 WORD PROBLEMS

$15.92
$0.51

$4.65	.44
14.98	4.6
2213.7	$8.72
14.8	$0.32